DEM●S

Demos is an independent think-tank committed to radical thinking on the long-term problems facing the UK and other advanced industrial societies.

It aims to develop the ideas – both theoretical and practical – that will help to shape the politics of the 21st century, and to improve the breadth and quality of political debate.

Demos publishes books and a quarterly journal and undertakes substantial empirical and policy-oriented research projects. Demos is a registered charity.

In all its work Demos brings together people from a wide range of backgrounds in business, academia, government, the voluntary sector and the media to share and cross-fertilise ideas and experiences.

For further information and subscription details please write to:
Demos
9 Bridewell Place
London, EC4V 6AP
Telephone: 0171 353 4479
Facsimile: 0171 353 4481
email: mail@demos.demon.co.uk

Public, Private or Community

What next for the NHS?

Chris Ham

DEM⊙S

First published in 1996 by
Demos
9 Bridewell Place
London EC4V 6AP
Telephone: 0171 353 4479
Facsimile: 0171 353 4481
e-mail: mail@demos.demon.co.uk
© Demos 1996

All rights reserved
Paper No. 24
ISBN 1 898309 23 X
Printed in Great Britain by
EG Bond Ltd
Designed by Esterson Lackersteen
Typeset by Joanna Wade
Thanks to Adrian Taylor

Contents

Acknowledgements

I would like to thank a number of people for helpful comments on earlier drafts. They include Nicholas Deakin, Robert Maxwell and John Stewart. I have also benefited from the advice and comments of Geoff Mulgan and Perri 6 of Demos. The arguments here have grown out of my work in the last ten years and have been influenced by colleagues at the University of Birmingham and the managers and staff from within the NHS with whom I have worked. At the Health Services Management Centre, Anne van der Salm and Sarah Stewart have provided excellent administrative support, including tidying up my word processing into a form suitable for publication. Thanks are due to the Joseph Rowntree Foundation and the OECD for permission to reproduce figures from their publications. I alone am responsible for the final text.

Chris Ham
Birmingham
September 1996

Introduction

Health care systems worldwide are in a state of flux because of the pressures arising from demographic changes and developments in medical technology, higher expectations on the part of patients and service users, and policies to contain or reduce public expenditure on health services. Policy makers in the health sector have responded by implementing a wide range of initiatives to reform the financing and delivery of health care. The United Kingdom has been at the forefront of these developments but is only one of many examples to be found around the world.

What distinguishes the UK is the rapid process of change which has occurred in the period since 1991. This has transformed the NHS from a traditional, bureaucratic, hierarchical organisation to a contract-based system centred on a separation of purchaser and provider responsibilities. Competition has been used as well as planning to stimulate improvements in performance. Building on earlier reforms to strengthen the management of health services by importing ideas from the best run companies, the effect has been to turn the NHS into a social business.

For the health policy analyst, the central question is:

what has been the impact of these changes and what are the prospects for the future? The difficulty in answering this question is the absence of systematic data on the effect of the reforms. This stems in large part from the refusal of the Thatcher government to establish any formal evaluations. While there have been a number of independent studies on particular aspects of the reforms,[1] there remain large gaps in our knowledge. There are also competing and often conflicting interpretations of the limited data that are available. For these reasons there is little consensus in the health policy community on the shape of the balance sheet resulting from the reforms.

I argue that there are two key issues facing health services in the UK. First, how should the reforms initiated by the Thatcher government be taken forward, whether or not there is a change of administration at the next election? And second, what are the options in the longer term? Will the private finance initiative result in the privatisation of health service provision? And given the pressures to contain public spending and to cut taxes, will it be possible to maintain a national health service free at the point of use and available to the whole population, or will more radical alternatives for reform have to be considered?

On the basis of the evidence available, this essay contends that policy towards the NHS in the immediate future should be guided by a genuine and statutory separation of purchaser and provider roles. Health care providers should have devolved responsibility for management to enable decisions to be taken as close to the patient as possible. There should also continue to be an independent purchasing or commissioning authority able to plan services on the basis of the population's health needs.[2] The main aim of the purchaser/provider system should be to ensure accountability for the use of resources and not to promote competition. Purchasers and providers must work together on a collaborative basis to stimulate improvements in performance. Different models of GP involvement in commissioning should be supported, including accountable fundholding. Transaction costs should be reduced by moving away from the annual contracting cycle to long-term contracting relationships.

Looking beyond the immediate future, the main challenge is to ensure that basic social goals are achieved in an era in which state monopoly provision is being questioned and when the more ambitious claims of Thatcherism have been discredited. Public financing and government regulation are essential if these goals are to be realised. New forms of service delivery need to be explored, and old forms rediscovered, while public financing is increasingly supplemented by alternative forms of funding. If taxation remains as the principal means of paying for health care, but is insufficient to meet all demands, then enhanced individual contributions in the context of public financing are the best way of filling the gap.

The same arguments apply to service provision. The alternative to state-owned health services is not the privatisation of everything. It is the space between the public and private that is important and in this space there are many opportunities for innovative forms of organisation to emerge. These organisations have the potential to be much more user-oriented and responsive than public sector agencies have often been in the past. This means building on the contribution of voluntary organisations and reinvigorating the role of intermediate institutions. The benefits of such an approach include not only more innovative and responsive service delivery but also a renewed commitment of individuals to each other's well-being and a rebuilding of community solidarity.

The role of government in the future should be to maintain taxation as the main source of health service funding and to regulate the provision of care. Government will also have responsibility for ensuring that the contributions made by individuals to the funding of health and social care are sufficient. The role of government as regulator is crucial in guaranteeing that all groups in society have access to necessary medical care and that high standards of provision are maintained. Not least, government will be responsible for avoiding the problems which arose before the state became the main provider of health services. These problems include market failure and fragmentation in service provision. This calls for new skills on the part of those in government and will take time to evolve.

As the regulator, government will need to ensure that a proper balance is struck between planning and competition. The old NHS demonstrated the weaknesses of centralised planning and it would be foolish to seek to return to this system. Equally, the shortcomings of markets in health care are well documented. The middle way between planning and competition is called contestability. In a contestable health service, the emphasis is placed on co-operation and co-ordination but with the option of moving to alternative providers if other means of improving performance do not work. This provides the incentive to ensure the efficient use of public resources while at the same time enabling services to be properly co-ordinated. Contestability assumes that government as regulator will continue to oversee the financing and provision of health care at a national level but that there will be considerable local freedom in determining the shape of service delivery. It also involves a key role for health authorities as commissioning agencies.

The challenge is to move beyond traditional dichotomies of public versus private, collective versus individual responsibility, planning versus markets, and centralisation versus decentralisation. A new synthesis is needed in which government does better by doing less.

Why was change necessary?

The record of the NHS since its establishment in 1948 is impressive. For a level of expenditure that is low in international terms, the NHS delivers more or less comprehensive health care to the whole population. Access to most health services does not depend on ability to pay and care is available in close proximity to where the vast majority of the population live. A particular strength of the NHS is the existence of general practitioners (GPs) as the first point of contact when a patient needs help or advice. The role of GPs as gatekeepers helps to explain the success of the NHS in containing costs and at the same time ensures continuity of care for patients. The NHS has also made the services of specialists more widely available through the network of district general hospitals. This is supplemented by the provision of highly specialised diagnosis and treatment in tertiary centres planned on a regional or sub-regional basis. The quality of care available within the NHS is generally held to be good and levels of patient satisfaction have traditionally been high.

Notwithstanding these achievements, the NHS suffers from a number of weaknesses. During the 1980s attention focused particularly on variations in performance between hospitals and evidence of inefficiency in the use of resources. In parallel there was growing concern about the length of time patients had to wait for non-urgent hospital treatment and the lack of responsiveness of service providers to patients. The emergence of a more articulate and demanding generation of service users also highlighted the limited choices available to patients in some parts of the NHS. Notwithstanding the benefits of central and regional planning of health care provision, it was increasingly apparent that there was a lack of incentives for health care providers to improve their performance and to respond to the demands of patients. Nowhere was this better illustrated than in relation to the efficiency trap facing hospitals whose budgets, fixed at the beginning of each year, were insensitive to changes in productivity during the year. In effect, these hospitals were penalised if they increased the number of patients treated because their income was constant while their expenditure rose. Global budgets for hospitals may have helped in controlling costs at the macro level but they offered little incentive for those providing care to improve efficiency at the micro level.

Increasing awareness of the cumulative effect of these deficiencies led Margaret Thatcher to announce a review of the NHS on the Panorama television programme in January 1988. While the proximate cause of the Thatcher review was a crisis of funding of hospitals in many parts of the NHS, and a number of well-publicised examples of patients, including children, having to wait for treatment, the underlying cause was the perceived need for a more fundamental reappraisal of the financing and delivery of health services.

The challenges facing the NHS in the 1980s made change not only inevitable but also desirable. Some commentators tend to argue that the old NHS had no blemishes and represented a golden age in the provision of health care in the UK. According to this perspective, any departure from the 1948 model was a step in the wrong direction and threatened to undermine the principles on which the NHS was founded. This was often linked to the argument that the only flaw in the old NHS was a shortage of funds. The most urgent need was therefore to increase the resources made available by the government and to fine tune the organisation of health care to improve the way in which these resources were used.

While there is undoubtedly some validity in these arguments, they fail to address a number of more deep-seated problems. Foremost among these is the phenomenon of provider capture. To a greater extent than many other public services, health care tends to be dominated by the staff responsible for providing services. Among these staff, the medical profession is particularly powerful. As volumes of research into NHS decision making have demonstrated,[3] doctors have traditionally exerted a great deal of influence over the allocation of resources and the delivery of care. To exaggerate only slightly, services have sometimes been run more for the convenience of staff than patients, and priorities have often reflected professional preferences rather than what the public wants. The voice of patients and the community has not been heard very strongly in the past and the emphasis on a collective approach to service provision has served to weaken the rights and choices of individual service users.

Another consequence of provider capture has been the dominance of the medical model of health care and the emphasis given to treating illness rather than improving health. It is this that has given rise to the argument that the NHS is really a sickness service and not a health service. In truth the NHS was set up both to maintain and improve the population's health and to provide necessary medical care when people become ill. In practice the latter function has come to predominate and society is well served by a comprehensive range of medical care facilities. Yet with many of the causes of ill health not amenable to medical intervention, the importance of action outside the health sector to improve health is increasingly recognised. In this respect the record of the UK is less impressive, and much remains to be done within the NHS to prevent illness and to encourage individuals to adopt healthy lifestyles. The organisation of the NHS after 1948 placed greater emphasis on the development of health services than the promotion of health and this made it difficult to give priority to disease prevention.

The challenge facing the Thatcher review was to find a way of reforming the NHS which enabled its weaknesses to be tackled and its strengths preserved. After an initial phase of investigating alternative options for financing health care, which quite rightly led to the conclusion that the system of tax funding should not be changed, the review focused on the delivery of health care.[4] Inspired in part by the ideas of the American economist, Alain Enthoven,[5] and in part by similar changes introduced into other parts of the public sector such as education, the review proposed the introduction of competitive principles. This was to be achieved by moving away from the bureaucratic, hierarchical structure established in 1948 and refined in the reorganisations of 1974 and 1982, towards a more pluralistic system centred on a separation of purchaser and provider responsibilities. The aim was to create a market between providers in order to stimulate greater efficiency and responsiveness on the supply side. This was linked to a system in which money was to follow patients in order to overcome the efficiency trap facing hospitals and to reward providers who competed successfully in the market.

Contrary to some expectations, there were no proposals to move away from a commitment to universality and comprehensiveness. Nor, as indicated earlier, was the method of funding health services to be altered. While this was a disappointment to right-wing think-tanks like the Institute of Economic Affairs, paradoxically it did little to reassure groups on the left who feared that the Thatcher government's proposals were the first step on the road to privatising health care (however this was defined). This fear was fuelled by the vocabulary used to present and debate the reforms. The language of markets and competition was alien to many of those used to the established tradition of planning and management and was interpreted as heralding a move towards a US style health system, even though this was denied by government spokespeople. The belief that there was a hidden agenda guiding the reforms persisted into the implementation phase and it is an issue to which we shall return further on.

The Thatcher reforms

The results of the Thatcher review were published in January 1989. In line with a promise made by Mrs Thatcher, this was almost exactly one year from the time the review was set up. One of the consequences of this tight timetable was that the proposals contained in *Working for Patients*,[6] the government's white paper on the NHS, were sketched in broad outline only. Further details followed shortly afterwards in a series of working papers, but it was clear from an early stage that the white paper had been written in some haste and that the implications had not been fully thought through. In this sense, implementation of the reforms has involved policy making on the hoof.[7] This has meant that a great deal of power rested in the hands of civil servants and the health service managers responsible for leading implementation of the changes. To a large extent policy was made as it was implemented, resulting in a period of experimentation and innovation almost unprecedented in the history of the NHS. There could be no starker contrast than with Keith Joseph's reorganisation of the NHS in 1974 which was planned in the minutest detail and which left nothing to chance.

It followed from this that the proposals set out in

Working for Patients had a number of unplanned and unanticipated consequences.[8] Thus, while they were presented as proposals designed to introduce competition into the provision of health services, they also led to a renewed focus on public health issues. This arose directly out of the separation of purchaser and provider responsibilities. The establishment of health authorities as purchasers of health care operating at arm's length from hospitals created an incentive for these authorities to think in terms of the population they served and not simply the services they managed. This was reinforced by the move to fund health authorities on a resident population basis. As a consequence, the new health authorities developed local strategies to improve the health of their populations as well as to strengthen the delivery of health services. These developments were supported by the publication of a national health strategy for England in 1992.[9] In this way, a start was made in tackling one of the weaknesses of the old NHS – its emphasis on responding to sickness rather than improving health.

Another unanticipated effect of the reforms was the rise to prominence of primary care. In one sense this was not a new development as primary care has always been a key element within the NHS. The NHS reforms proceeded in parallel with the imposition of a new contract on general practitioners and policies designed to strengthen family health services. Nevertheless, the separation of purchaser and provider roles led health authorities to pay greater attention to the views of GPs than had been the case in the past. With GPs deciding where to refer patients for treatment, and health authorities placing contracts with hospitals for the provision of care, it was essential that there should be a dialogue to co-ordinate the two sets of decisions. Out of this dialogue GPs gained more influence over the allocation of resources by health authorities. And in the case of GPs who chose to hold a budget as fundholders, they were given the purchasing power to negotiate directly with hospitals. The result was not only to produce changes in the provision of secondary care but also to enable a wider range of services to be delivered by GPs in a primary care setting. The central role of primary care was emphasised in a consultation document published by the government in 1996 which set out a range of proposals for further strengthening the position of GPs within the NHS.

This was supported by a further unanticipated effect of the reforms: the establishment of a research and development function, including a major emphasis on evidence-based medicine and health technology assessment. Again, this was not foreshadowed in *Working for Patients* and its long-term significance became clear only slowly. It was, however, of considerable importance in providing purchasers with ammunition to fire in their negotiations with providers.

The emphasis here was less on using the purchaser/ provider system to stimulate competition than on encouraging health authorities and fundholders to question the effectiveness and cost effectiveness of medical interventions. The underlying rationale was that there was scope for obtaining better value for money in the use of NHS resources by making use of research-based evidence in deciding which services to purchase. Among other things, this led to a more critical appraisal of the use of common surgical procedures where the evidence suggested that operations were often done unnecessarily and inappropriately.

The emphasis on public health, primary care and evidence-based medicine challenged those running hospital and community health services. Doctors and managers in these services had traditionally been in the driving seat in setting priorities within the NHS. The creation of NHS trusts to take responsibility for hospital and community health services meant that their influence came to be exerted at one step removed from those responsible for purchasing health care. The latter were therefore able to take a more independent and detached view of health needs and to deploy their budgets accordingly. Over time, this resulted in a gradual but perceptible shift in the balance of power within the NHS. Hospital doctors and managers were held more accountable for their performance and health authorities and GPs gained in influence.

Despite the rhetoric of patient choice contained in *Working for Patients*, in reality the reforms did little to change the position of service users. The use of block contracts between purchasers and providers meant that in many cases money did not follow the patient as these contracts did not provide incentives for increased productivity. The result was reduced choice for the patients of non-fundholding GPs whose referrals to hospital had to fit in with the decisions of health authorities on where to place contracts, whereas before the reforms GPs had almost complete freedom to choose where to send patients. GP fundholders were an exception to this and their preference for cost and volume and cost per case contracts did result in money following the patient. Yet with fundholders covering a minority of the population and buying only a defined list of services, their ability to achieve improvements in services for patients was limited. Indeed, as research demonstrated, although some fundholders were innovative purchasers, others were much more cautious and the overall impact on patient care was therefore modest.[10]

The main impact of the shift in the balance of power within the NHS was to create a greater capacity for tackling weaknesses in service delivery. In place of the old structure in which health authorities and managers had few levers to improve performance, the purchaser/ provider system had the effect of unfreezing established relationships and introducing a deeper level of questioning of professional practices. The opportunity in some parts of the country to move contracts between providers also acted as a stimulus to change. Those running NHS trusts were in this way put in the position of having to market their services to purchasers and to agree on standards for service delivery. The contracts negotiated between purchasers and providers made these standards transparent and provided a series of benchmarks for comparing performance. The publication of performance tables by the Department of Health setting out the achievements of NHS trusts in delivering the targets established in the Patient's Charter was one manifestation of this.[11]

The impact on services was evident in reductions in waiting times for hospital treatment and increases in the number of patients treated. The exact scale of these changes and the reasons for them are more difficult to discern. Analysis is complicated by the higher than average growth in NHS expenditure during the early 1990s and alterations in data recording and collection systems.[12] And in the case of waiting time reductions, this had less to do with the market than with the political priority attached to this objective. With ministers making it clear that waiting time reductions were not negotiable, strong pressure was placed on managers to ensure that the targets were met. In this sense, old fashioned Stalinism rather than free-market liberalism was mainly responsible. This reflected a trend in other parts of the NHS to centralise power in order to drive through government policies. The paradox is that centralisation on some issues went hand in hand with decentralisation on others in a style of political management which defied simple categorisation.

This was particularly evident in the case of GP fundholding. More than any other single element in the reforms, fundholding epitomised the government's desire to unlock established patterns of service provision and to drive change from the bottom up. Research into the impact of fundholding has described the impact of the scheme on the prescribing of drugs, referrals to hospital, the responsiveness of hospitals to GPs and their patients, and the delivery of services in primary care. Interpretations of this research do, however, vary greatly. While some analysts conclude that fundholders have proved more effective purchasers than health authorities, others remain to be convinced that the benefits of fundholding outweigh the costs.[13]

Perhaps not surprisingly, the government views fundholding as a success and has announced an expansion of the scheme to enable a number of pilot practices to buy all services for their patients, not only the limited range of services included in the original version of fundholding. At the same time, the scope of standard fundholding has been expanded and a new option of community fundholding has been introduced for smaller practices.

Despite these moves, critics maintain that fundholders have undermined equity in the NHS by negotiating quicker access to hospital services for their patients regardless of clinical need. There are also concerns that in the longer term, as budgetary constraints begin to tighten, fundholders may discriminate against patients who are older and sicker. The absence of systematic research evaluating the effects of fundholding in comparison with health authority purchasing makes it difficult to assess whether the achievements of fundholders have been replicated by health authorities and hampers informed discussion of different models of purchasing.

What this brief review suggests is that any efficiency gains resulting from the reforms have been achieved at the expense of equity losses. Beyond this, there has been a refocusing on public health, primary care and evidence-based medicine. Less tangibly, the reforms have introduced a new dynamic into the management of health services. This has resulted in a shift in the balance of power and a greater capacity for addressing weaknesses in service delivery.

Set against these gains, the separation of purchaser and provider responsibilities has led to an increase in management costs. Figures released by the Labour Party suggest that expenditure on administration in England increased by £1.5bn in real terms between 1988/89 and 1994/95. This is due in part to the appointment of an additional 20,000 senior managers and in part to an increase in clerical staff. Also some of the extra costs of NHS management result from a reclassification of nursing and other professional posts into the management grade.

The need to spend more money on management derives from the separation of purchaser and provider responsibilities and the policy of strengthening management in NHS trusts. In addition, the negotiation of annual contracts between purchasers and providers has led to the employment of extra administrative staff whose services were not needed in the old NHS. Fundholding has added to the complexity of contracting because NHS trusts have to negotiate contracts with a large number of small purchasers. Fundholders also receive management allowances to help them run their budgets. The investment made in management has brought benefits in terms of improved information about the cost and quality of service but has been criticised across the political spectrum for diverting money from direct patient care.

The government has responded to concerns about the rising costs of management by streamlining the organisation of the NHS and reducing the number of managers. This includes replacing Regional Health Authorities with regional offices of the NHS Executive, merging District Health Authorities and Family Health Services Authorities in England and Wales, and setting tough targets for management costs in health authorities and trusts. Also, in response to an efficiency scrutiny into the burdens of paperwork in NHS trusts and health authorities, ministers have announced a move towards longer-term contracts and a simplification of the system of extra-contractual referrals. Running counter to these developments, the expansion of fundholding will increase management costs.

Overall, it appears that a contract-based system is more expensive to administer than the integrated system it replaced. What remains open to dispute is whether the benefits outweigh the additional costs that have been incurred. Summarising the evidence in this way illustrates why many commentators conclude that at this stage the jury is still out on whether the reforms really are working for patients.

Consensus, conflict and the NHS reforms

The Labour Party's policy on the health service has gradually been modified in response to the changes introduced by the Thatcher government. From a position of outright opposition to *Working for Patients* in 1989, Labour has come to accept that some of the changes that have been introduced are worth maintaining and it has promised to adapt others rather than 'turn the clock back'. This was stated clearly in *Renewing the NHS*[14] and was reiterated in Tony Blair's speech at the June 1996 conference of the National Association of Health Authorities and Trusts. Labour's stance reflects not only the modernising influence of its new leadership but also recognition that a future Labour government will be able to use the reforms contained in *Working for Patients* to pursue its own ends. In their policy ends, there is a good deal of common ground between the two major parties. The priority attached to the national health strategy, a primary care-led NHS, research and development, evidence-based medicine, community care, efficiency in the use of resources, and improvements in the quality of services to patients is shared across the political spectrum. The issues of most potential dispute centre on the merits or otherwise of the purchaser/provider system, the future role of markets in health care, and GP fundholding. In relation to these issues, it is important to be clear as to the lessons which have been learnt in the last five years.

The purchaser/provider system

Taking the purchaser/provider system first, evidence from the period since 1991 suggests that it is this element of the Thatcher reforms that has been central to the ability of managers and others to challenge established practices and bring about improvements in the use of resources. Without this change many of the most positive effects of the reforms would not have been realised. Three aspects of the purchaser/provider system are especially important. First, freedom has been given to NHS trusts to manage their own affairs. The devolution of power to providers has unleashed a great deal of enterprise and energy on the part of those running hospital and community services. Freed from interference from above, except as demanded by the arrangements for holding trusts accountable for their performance, many trusts have taken the initiative to increase their efficiency and improve their responsiveness to service users. In this way, local management of health services has been one of the most positive changes to have resulted from the Thatcher reforms.

Second, the purchaser/provider system has enabled health authorities to use their resources unencumbered by day-to-day responsibility for running hospitals. This has allowed the doctors and managers in health authorities to focus on the health of the populations they serve. Whereas in the past health authorities were preoccupied with managing the hospitals for which they were responsible, there is now the opportunity to think more broadly about patterns of death and illness in each community and how these can best be addressed. This may mean an investment in health care but it could also involve working with other public agencies to tackle the problems which give rise to ill health. The point about the purchaser/provider system from a health authority perspective is that it has gradually transformed health authorities from inward-looking organisations concerned with operational responsibilities to outward-looking agencies charged with using their resources for the benefit of the populations they serve.

Third, the separation of purchaser and provider responsibilities has made the way in which money is spent in the NHS more transparent. This is because the contracts or service agreements negotiated between purchasers and providers demonstrate the requirements placed on providers by purchasers and the standards of care that providers are expected to deliver. Transparency has helped to promote greater accountability by enabling health authorities, GPs and interested sections of the public, like community health councils, to assess performance against contract. To be sure, the complexity and density of many contract documents does not always facilitate transparency but compared with the old NHS in which hospitals were funded via global budgets with few strings attached the purchaser/provider system represents a significant step forward.

The value of this system hinges in large part on the fact that there is a statutory separation of roles. In the early stages of the reforms health authorities prepared for the introduction of NHS trusts by setting up arm's length management relationships with their hospitals. This illustrated the difficulties of 'holding on while letting go'.[15] While health authorities continued to carry ultimate responsibility for the services in their areas, they served as the focus of political and public attention when controversial matters arose. Inevitably, this drew health authority managers into decisions concerning the management of services. Not only did this inhibit the emergence of a culture of devolved management within hospitals, it also made it difficult for health authorities to focus on the populations they served. This suggests that a purchaser/provider system will work effectively only if there is a genuine division of roles in which separate statutory bodies are established to take responsibility for purchasing and providing respectively. Arm's length management within the ambit of a health authority runs the risk of placing power back in the hands of secondary care providers and weakening the incentive for health authorities to work closely with GPs and to maintain a focus on public health.

One of the weaknesses of health authorities is that their membership often lacks legitimacy in the eyes of the population. There is a democratic deficit in the organisation of the NHS which undermines the credibility of health authorities as 'champions of the people' – to borrow the phrase used by health ministers. This needs to be tackled by widening the membership of health authorities and appointing a cross section of people drawn from the communities served. Although there are theoretical attractions in giving local authorities responsibility for commissioning health services or establishing separately elected health authorities for this purpose, along the lines of the Nordic model, this would need to be linked with a greater capacity for raising resources at a local level. If local taxation were to come onto the political agenda then the option of placing the NHS in the hands of elected authorities should be carefully considered, but until this happens changes to the present system of appointed authorities should be the focus of attention.

The role of markets

The second issue is the role of markets in health care. There is no inherent connection between a purchaser/provider system and the existence of competition, although these issues are often confused in the debate about health care reform. Not least, it is argued that a purchaser/provider system will inevitably result in a market developing and those who oppose competition use this argument also to oppose a purchaser/provider system. The thesis underlying this essay, expressed at its most simple, is that it is possible and indeed desirable to maintain a statutory purchaser/provider split but that markets have only a limited part to play. The logic here is that the main purpose of the purchaser/provider split, as argued earlier, is to ensure accountability on the part of providers to purchasers and this does not in itself imply that there should be competition between providers for the resources controlled by purchasers. Put another way, the purchaser/provider system is justified not on the basis of economic theories which advocate the primacy of markets but in terms of the organisational politics of health care. It is the need to find a way of holding providers to account and of avoiding provider capture that lends strength to the arguments for a separation of purchaser and provider responsibilities.

Does this therefore mean that there should be no role for markets in health care? Not quite. In a publicly funded health care system like the NHS it is essential that there are real incentives to drive improvements in performance. It was a significant shortcoming of the old NHS that these incentives were weak or non-existent. Indeed, the efficiency trap facing hospitals, discussed earlier, introduced perverse incentives into the management of the NHS. The promise of the Thatcher reforms was that providers would be rewarded for improvements in efficiency through a system in which money followed the patient. In fact the money has not followed the patient in most parts of the NHS and the promise therefore remains unfulfilled. As we have noted, it is also the case that the current contracting system carries high transaction costs. For these reasons health ministers have recently placed less emphasis on competition and have instead stressed the need for partnership in the NHS combined with longer-term contracts between purchasers and providers.

These are pragmatic and sensible moves which reflect the assimilation of experience from the initial stages of the reforms and the limits in promoting provider competition in the NHS. They also reflect developments at a local level which are focusing increasingly on the establishment of 'preferred provider' relationships in which purchasers seek to work closely with their major providers on a continuing basis. In these ways contracting relationships have come to be seen by many as more important than contract documents, although a vast effort continues to be put into contract negotiation and monitoring.

The role of markets which is beginning to emerge is less to act as the principle by which resources are allocated in the NHS than to be one of the levers available to purchasers for improving performance. In other words, the starting point is that increases in efficiency and improvements in responsiveness are best achieved by purchasers and providers working together to deal with issues of common concern. Only if this approach fails to produce results will purchasers consider moving contracts to alternative providers. However, this threat is ever present in the purchaser/provider system and the knowledge that purchasers may move contracts and resources is meant to act as a stimulus to providers to be responsive and to meet the demands of purchasers. For the threat to be credible it has to be exercised from time to time, but this is quite different from competitive tendering which in effect uses market testing on a continuing basis to keep providers on their toes and to exert downward pressure on costs. As experience in the NHS since 1991 shows, it is not necessary for purchasers to move large volumes of contracts on a regular basis for changes in behaviour to occur. Both health authorities and fundholders have demonstrated that even small shifts can make a difference, sending out a signal that a purchaser means business and creating an incentive for providers to keep the cost and quality of their services permanently under review.

This approach is based on *contestability* rather than market testing.[16] While there are those who would no doubt contend that there is little difference between the two and that both are forms of competition, the argument of this essay is that there is a key distinction to be made and that contestability is the preferred approach. Contestability is an idea worth pursuing because it combines the need for a planned approach with incentives to stimulate providers to use resources for the benefit of service users and those who purchase on their behalf. In essence, contestability provides the spur to improvements in performance which has often been lacking in the NHS while acknowledging the need for collaboration and partnership between purchasers and providers.

Fundholding

The third issue is the future of GP fundholding. While the evidence on fundholding remains inconclusive, it has attracted support from some unlikely quarters for demonstrating what can be achieved when entrepreneurial groups of professionals are given the purchasing power to achieve changes in services for patients.[17] Alongside fundholding, alternative models of involving GPs in the decisions taken by health authorities in their purchasing activities have developed. These include locality sensitive commissioning, the setting up of GP commissioning groups, and the use of GPs on a sessional basis to advise health authorities.[18] As a result, decisions on the use of NHS budgets are more primary care focused, resulting in changes to both the delivery of hospital services and the provision of care by GPs. There is now a cross party consensus on the importance of primary care-led commissioning in the NHS (although the words used to describe it might be different), notwithstanding what appear to be irreconcilable differences on fundholding per se.

Fundholding has so far proved anathema to the Labour Party because of its adverse effects on equity, the transaction costs it generates, the possibility of risk selection by fundholders, lack of accountability for the use of resources, and concerns about the level of savings made by fundholders and how these savings are used. These factors have been more persuasive than the argument of some analysts that GPs are more effective purchasers than health authorities. And although Labour's policy on the NHS seeks to encourage a range of alternative approaches to involving GPs in commissioning, these approaches do not at this point extend to fundholding in its present form. The paradox here is that just as there appears to be increasing convergence between GP-focused commissioning and health authority-centred commissioning, so the opportunity to emphasise the middle ground is being closed down. This applies equally to the government which is actively promoting fundholding as the model of choice for commissioning and which has been lukewarm about alternatives such as locality sensitive commissioning.

The blinkered approach of politicians of both parties is to be regretted for the argument ought not to be whether health authorities or fundholders are the better purchasers but rather how the best features of different approaches can be combined. In the case of the Conservatives, this requires acknowledgment that not all GPs want to be fundholders and even among those who have chosen this route there is concern about the workload and the impact of budgetary constraints in the longer term. Also important is the evidence produced by the Audit Commission that the costs of fundholding so far outweigh the benefits.[19] As far as Labour is concerned, the challenge is to explore whether the benefits of fundholding can be retained as part of a more accountable commissioning process in which health authorities are clearly identified as the strategic commissioners in each area. For example, one of the first experiments in total purchasing by fundholders operates as a sub-committee of the local health authority.[20] The GPs in the project work hand in hand with the health authority and their budget is set on the same basis as that of the health authority to ensure equity in resource allocation. The project covers almost all of the population living in the locality and in this way is able to overcome concerns about inequities in access to health care in the area. Refinement of this kind of approach, which is in any case very similar to many of the GP commissioning and locality commissioning approaches endorsed by Labour, has much to commend it. This could include introducing tighter regulations governing the use of savings in fundholders' budgets and rules to ensure that improvements in services achieved by fundholders are extended to all GPs.

What this suggests is that while the Labour Party's approach has shown a refreshing willingness to examine the impact of the Thatcher reforms in an open-minded manner, there are nevertheless areas in which more work and clarity are needed. On the basis of the admittedly incomplete and contested evidence that is available, it can be suggested that policy towards the NHS in the future should be guided by:

● a commitment to a genuine and statutory separation of purchaser and provider roles;

● development of devolved management of providers to ensure that decisions are taken as close to the patient as possible;

● support for the continuation of an independent commissioning or purchasing authority able to plan on the basis of health needs;

● recognition that the purchaser/provider system should be used to ensure accountability for the use of resources, not to promote competition;

● acknowledgment that the purchaser/provider system should encourage collaborative arrangements in which purchasers and providers work together on a long-term basis;

● a commitment to contestability as a way of stimulating improvements in performance and providing incentives for efficiency;

● support for different models of GP involvement in commissioning, including accountable fundholding; and

● a commitment to reduce transaction costs by moving away from the annual contracting cycle to long-term contracting relationships.

The point of emphasising these organisational issues is to provide the means of implementing a strategy for the NHS which gives priority to the improvement of the population's health as well as developments in health services. The latter objective encompasses the strengthening of primary care, improving the quality of service provision, ensuring efficiency in the use of resources, and promoting the use of effective and cost-effective medical procedures. The rationale for advocating a purchaser/provider system centred on collaboration but allowing for contestability is that this is likely to be the best way of giving priority to these policies. To return to the starting point of this essay, if the problem of provider capture is acknowledged to be real, then it is essential that there is an effective countervailing force in the form of a strategic and independent commissioning authority. This authority must be able to work with general practitioners and others in deciding on the best use of the resources at its disposal. It also needs to have sufficient levers to promote change. If such an authority can work within a framework of local as well as national accountability, then it will be better placed to act as a champion of the people.

By moving in this direction, it ought to be possible to produce further savings in management costs, although it is always likely to be more expensive to administer a purchaser/provider system than an integrated health service. The key point to emphasise here is that a modern health service needs to be well run. Unnecessary administration and paperwork can be reduced by simplifying NHS contracting but there is no escaping the need to ensure that staff and other resources are effectively managed. To that extent, attention should concentrate not only on the costs of management but also on the relationship between these costs and the results achieved in different hospitals and health authorities. A focus on outcomes rather than just inputs is needed to raise the debate to a new level.[21]

The longer term

What are the drivers of change which are likely to affect future developments? To begin with, there is the continuing power of the health care professions – especially doctors – in shaping the direction of service provision. Recent reforms have altered the balance of power between general practitioners and hospital doctors, but medical views remain important in explaining how resources are allocated and priorities set. At the same time, the rise of consumerism in health care has started to challenge professional autonomy and has led to demands for higher standards of care in a number of areas. This in turn has run into the priority attached to evidence-based medicine with its assumption that resources should be allocated on the basis of need rather than demand.

Alongside these developments, greater emphasis has been placed on the responsibility of individuals to look after themselves in reducing avoidable mortality and morbidity. Paradoxically, there is also increasing concern at the re-emergence of infectious diseases and the need for public health measures at the community level to respond to these diseases. The changing pattern of illness in the population, coupled with the resources needed to deal with the growing burden of chronic diseases, will add to the pressures on constrained health care budgets. The challenge for policy makers in the longer term is therefore to find ways of strengthening the accountability of the health care professions, increasing responsiveness of providers to services users, and balancing individual and community responsibility for improving health.

A range of options is discussed in the rest of this essay. In the case of service provision, these options include the privatisation of providers as well as their return to community ownership and control. As far as financing is concerned, the consequences of increasing private expenditure on health care are examined as are alternative approaches to rationing and priority setting. The essay argues that the debate about the future of health care needs to move beyond discussion of public versus private funding and provision. Government should continue to play a major part in overseeing the development of the health care system but increasingly this should be in partnership with individuals and communities. New ways of providing services need to be developed with a mixture of public and private funds being used to pay for services like long-term care which are currently not available to all those who need them within the NHS. The alternative to state monopoly health care is not the privatisation of everything. Instead, there is an opportunity to develop innovative solutions to current dilemmas by rediscovering old traditions and stimulating new thinking about the future direction of services.

Alternative futures

Where then are the NHS reforms leading? To the extent that policy has been driven from the bottom up and not the top down, the ultimate destination depends on how the new management arrangements are used by those working in the NHS. According to this perspective, the reforms represent an emergent strategy which will only become clear with the passage of time. Put more simply, policy makers have been making it up as they have been going along and any one of several outcomes is possible.[22] This depends not only on the local interpretation of the reforms but also on the steer provided by politicians. The emphasis placed by health ministers on partnership rather than competition and on a more collaborative approach to change is at least as important as the original aspirations of the architects of the changes to introduce a market into health care provision.

An alternative school of thought argues that the reforms are guided by a clear strategy designed to destabilise and ultimately to privatise service provision, but that this has not been made public. Thus, the separation of purchaser and provider roles and the establishment of NHS trusts is seen as a necessary pre-requisite to the privatisation of health care. In the longer term, it is argued, there will be a mixed economy of service provision in which the private or independent sector plays a much bigger part than at present. Privatisation in this context applies to the delivery rather than the financing of care, although it is suggested that the latter may also be more reliant on private sources with the passage of time. Some support for this argument was provided by the former Health Secretary, Virginia Bottomley, in an article in the *Independent* newspaper in August 1994:

'We start by recognising that we have, in effect, redefined what we mean by the National Health Service. The service should not be defined by who provides it, but by the fundamental principle which underpins their work: to provide care on the basis of clinical need and regardless of the ability to pay ... The precise nature of the services provided should increasingly become a matter for local decision. We should be open-minded about this ... In the NHS of the future we can expect to see a much greater diversity of provision. The independent sector will supply some services, including direct patient care, under contract to health authorities and fundholders.'[23]

This statement clearly indicates a move towards greater variety in the ownership and management of hospitals and related services. This implies that the NHS will be seen increasingly as a national health insurance organisation responsible for paying for health care but no longer the monopoly deliverer of health services to the population. As Mrs Bottomley notes in the same article, this has always been how general practice has been organised within the NHS. General practitioners have worked as independent contractors (or private practitioners) rather than salaried health service employees and they have provided services free to patients under contract to the NHS. Extending the logic of this argument implies that the providers of hospital and community health services will also operate as independent bodies, as already occurs when private hospitals, for example, provide services to NHS patients paid for by health authorities or fundholders. If this were to happen it would be a significant extension of current policies. Whether it will happen depends largely on the fate of the government's private finance initiative (PFI) which was launched in 1992 by the Chancellor of the Exchequer as a way of attracting private finance to pay for public sector projects.

The virtual organisation

Until recently the PFI was of marginal importance in the NHS, being confined mainly to schemes such as car parks and incinerators.[24] However, under a change of rules published in 1995, NHS trusts wishing to undertake major capital schemes are required to seek private finance before they can be considered for Treasury support. The rules also mark a significant development of the PFI in that they enable private finance to pay not only for the capital costs of NHS schemes but also for associated services. The only limit placed on this is that medical and nursing staff should remain in the employment of NHS trusts. Even in this case, however, there is uncertainty as to the scope of PFI projects with some NHS trusts including clinical services such as pathology within the ambit of PFI developments.

An analogy used by civil servants and NHS managers in discussing the initiative is revealing for what it says about the thinking of those closely involved in this area. The analogy is British Airways (BA). Why, it is argued, if BA can operate successfully by contracting out services such as aircraft maintenance, catering and leasing its aircraft cannot the NHS function in the same way? What matters about BA is that it employs its core staff – pilots and the cabin crew – and it has a strong market image. Most other aspects of its operation can be carried out independently under contract to BA. Applying the same logic to the NHS suggests that only clinical staff in direct contact with patients need to be in NHS employment and other services can be made available on the BA model by independent companies outside the NHS.

This is now happening as the first major PFI schemes in the NHS are put together. Special purpose companies are being formed as construction firms and companies involved in facilities management are established to bid for the estimated £2bn of work currently out to tender in this way (see Figure 1 opposite). Treasury rules require NHS trusts to advertise in the *Official Journal of the European Communities* for all major schemes. The government hopes that by bringing in private sector expertise there will be benefits for the NHS and added value from projects which may also involve hotel, shopping, housing and related developments. And the point of extending PFI beyond the capital costs of NHS schemes to the running of services is that this may enable the private sector to squeeze efficiency savings out of running services to justify the additional cost of raising capital from non-Treasury sources. Indeed public spending on NHS capital schemes has already been reduced significantly in anticipation of private finance being used to fund major developments. The 1996 consultation paper on primary care has, in effect, suggested an extension of this model from the hospital sector and support functions to primary care.

Contract structure

Figure 1

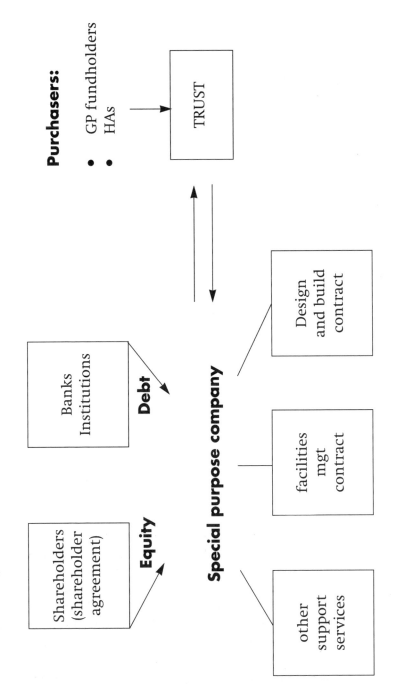

Purchasers:
- GP fundholders
- HAs

TRUST

Banks Institutions

Debt

Shareholders (shareholder agreement)

Equity

Special purpose company

Design and build contract

facilities mgt contract

other support services

The prospect is of the NHS as a virtual organisation. With bricks and mortar under private control, and an increasing number of staff employed outside the NHS, the traditional view of the NHS as the organisation that takes care of all our health care needs is no longer tenable. A network of relationships and agencies will increasingly replace the hierarchical bureaucracy that existed before 1991 and the NHS will combine public finance and public and private provision. The question is: does the abandonment of state monopoly service provision matter? Is it merely an example of the NHS adapting to changes affecting other sectors and modernising itself for the challenge of the new millennium? Or is it the beginning of the end of the post-war settlement in health care as the boundaries between public and private are blurred and privatisation in the health services becomes a reality? It is difficult to answer these questions because major PFI schemes are at an early stage of development in the NHS but they can be illuminated by considering how other countries order their health services.

Experience around the world suggests that the key to achieving universal coverage and access to comprehensive services is the assumption by government of responsibility for paying for health care. This may be combined with a variety of forms of ownership and employment patterns for staff – as demonstrated by the experience in Canada and in a number of western European countries where hospitals and other facilities are in the hands of non-governmental bodies and where doctors remain private practitioners or independent contractors. These systems are examples of the public contract model of health services provision, to use the terminology proposed by the OECD,[25] in contrast to the public integrated model which is how the NHS was run before 1991 (see Figures 2 and 3 on pages following).

In public contract systems there are various forms of ownership of hospitals. The general rule is that hospitals operate on a non-profit basis and they may be owned by local communities, religious and charitable agencies, or

Figure 2 - The Contract Model

Compulsory insurance with insurer/provider contracts

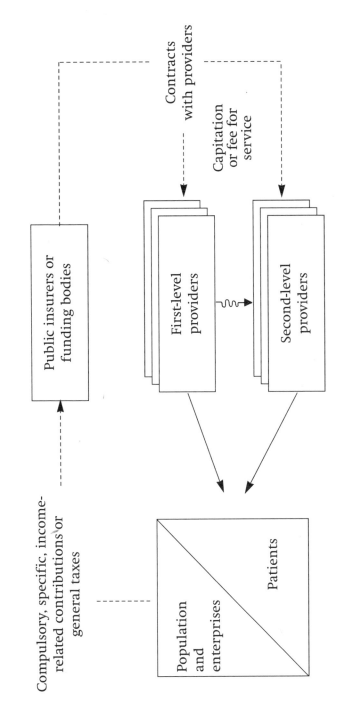

Source: OECD (1992)

Figure 3 - The Integrated Model

Compulsory insurance with integration between insurance and provision

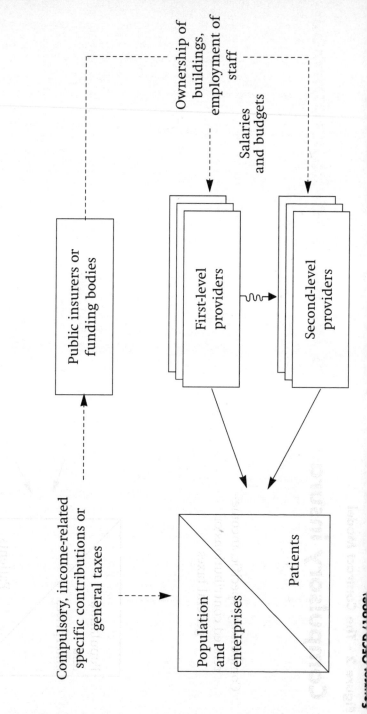

Ownership of buildings, employment of staff

Salaries and budgets

Public insurers or funding bodies

First-level providers

Second-level providers

Compulsory, income-related specific contributions or general taxes

Population and enterprises

Patients

Source: OECD (1992)

other bodies. In this sense, private ownership carries different connotations than in the UK where it is often used in contradistinction to public ownership and in terms which are implicitly if not explicitly unfavourable. In reality the debate about alternative forms of ownership and governance is a good deal more complex than often appears to be the case and the failure to acknowledge this seriously hampers the argument. Only in the United States are for-profit organisations major players in the health system and the United States is the one country whose experience has little to offer the UK.

In fact there is scope for a range of innovative approaches to emerge. Some of these could be as attractive to a Labour government as to the Conservatives. For example, the Co-operative Bank has published a report outlining opportunities for co-operatives to become involved in the provision of residential care.[26] There is no reason in principle why the same should not apply to hospital services. Indeed, a recent analysis of private medical care in the UK has proposed that the churches may have a part to play in service provision to counteract the threat to equity posed by the emergence of a market in health care.[27] Plans have also been put forward for the future use of St. Bartholomew's Hospital in London involving its establishment as a charitable institution independent of the NHS.[28] Even more radically, it has been suggested that community hospitals which are threatened with closure should be handed over to their communities who would take responsibility for their financing and management.[29] As these examples illustrate, proposals to increase the role of the voluntary sector and the community in service provision are already under active consideration and the importance of non-profit forms of service delivery is increasingly recognised.

A common point in many of these analyses is a concern that the values of a national health service may be undermined by the increasing involvement of commercial interests in PFI schemes and similar initiatives. It is certainly the case that financial institutions will not want to put their capital at risk through these kinds of investment and that they are attracted by the prospect of appropriate financial returns. This creates a danger that the pursuit of profit will make it difficult to maintain an ethos within the health service which is consistent with its public service responsibilities.

There are also doubts about the ability of the consortia of organisations now coming together to undertake PFI projects in the NHS to see these projects through to completion. These consortia are largely untried and untested and their use in a public service like the NHS is a gamble. A number of the construction companies involved in NHS PFI projects have already indicated their dissatisfaction with the complexity of the procedures, including the cost and time involved in preparing bids. This has led some companies to announce that they will not compete for further NHS projects at this stage.

The rules established by the Treasury require the private sector to bear some of the risk of privately financed schemes but how realistic this is and what will happen if the schemes fail is unclear. Indeed, the government has been forced to enact legislation to reassure private companies that their investments will be secure should an NHS trust be merged with another trust, yet even this has apparently failed to satisfy the banks who continue to be concerned by the extent of risk they are being asked to assume.

What is also uncertain is the impact that PFI may have on the running of hospitals. It is likely that private sector interests will wish to take a close interest in the management of services, including having a seat on the board and a say in the appointment of senior managers and doctors. This could have significant implications for accountability and control, but these have not been thought through. Therefore, the prospect of alternative forms of non-profit organisation entering the supply side has attractions, although the difficulty of rebuilding this kind of voluntary tradition should not be underestimated after almost fifty years of near state monopoly. In this sense, countries like Canada and the Netherlands which have adopted the public contract model and have built on their traditions of charitable, religious and community involvement have a natural advantage. Nevertheless, it may be possible to re-invigorate these traditions over time, drawing on experience in the hospice movement and other sectors such as the care of people with HIV and AIDS. As government also encourages the development of non-state provision of community care services, we are on the verge of rediscovering the importance of intermediate institutions as suppliers of health and welfare services.

There are, however, disadvantages in transforming the NHS into a virtual organisation. One of the reasons why hospitals were taken into public ownership in 1948 was that the co-existence of municipal and voluntary hospitals made it difficult to co-ordinate the provision of services. These hospitals also found it hard to balance their books and to acquire the equipment and facilities needed in a modern health service. As the hospital surveys carried out during the Second World War emphasised,[30] reorganisation was long overdue and this was one of the reasons why the post-war Labour government decided that nationalising hospitals was necessary. Notwithstanding Beveridge's support for voluntarism, the views of Aneurin Bevan carried the day. State ownership of hospitals was enacted by Parliament and centralised planning replaced local co-ordination as the means of ensuring that services were available where they were needed.

As new forms of organisation based on a more limited role for direct state provision and greater pluralism on the supply side are debated, it is important not to lose sight of these lessons from history. The innovation and liberation that may result from the emergence of a mixed economy of health care provision have to be weighed against the potential loss of co-ordination when ownership is no longer in public hands. The risk is that service provision will become increasingly fragmented and that public financing of health care will be insufficient to ensure that the NHS meets its objectives.

On the other hand, as Prochaska emphasises,[31] it is easy to exaggerate the weaknesses of the pre-war health service. The voluntary contribution was fundamental to the development of the NHS and it has continued to be important, albeit in a quite different context. There is therefore no reason why non-profit organisations should not once again play a part in service provision, so long as government is actively involved in regulation. This includes health authorities taking responsibility for the commissioning of services at a local level. Furthermore, the weaknesses of the pre-war health service may be overcome in part by the establishment of an agency to support the development of the voluntary sector and to provide access to capital funds. One source of these funds is the National Lottery which should be required to set aside part of its income specifically for capital investment in health care.

These arguments are not confined to health care but reflect a much broader debate about the future of the welfare state and the nature of democratic society. Of particular importance is the critique set out by Hirst[32] and others of the failures of both collectivist state socialism and free-market capitalism. Hirst articulates the case for 'associationalism' in which individual choice is combined with public welfare. At the heart of associationalism is a preference for voluntary organisations over bureaucracies because of their greater responsiveness and flexibility. Voluntary organisations are also favoured because they may provide a more effective way of involving citizens and users than state bureaucracies. This critique seeks to break the link between welfare and the state by suggesting that important social goals may be better achieved through voluntary self-governing associations than through centralised public agencies, of which the old NHS was a classic example.

To argue in this way is not to suggest a return to nineteenth century philanthropy. Rather, it is to make the point that some of the dichotomies which have dominated debate about welfare services may no longer be helpful and that there is an alternative way of thinking about the issues offering a synthesis of ideas which have previously been presented as contradictory. As Hirst argues:

'An associationalist welfare system ... offers greater empowerment (and) recognises that such empowerment cannot come from state centralism and the inevitable bureaucracy that accompanies it, but only from decentralisation and a degree of popular control. An associationalist welfare state would be decentralised and pluralistic, it would be divided into self-governing regions, into distinct and competing voluntary associations, and into different functionally-distinct service sectors. No single agency would have omnicompetent control over all the others, rather at best a limited and functionally-specific power of inspection, rule-setting or funding.'[33]

This approach rejects market-based solutions to health service funding and delivery as strongly as it criticises state solutions. In essence it argues for a system of 'thick welfare and thin collectivism' in which resources would be allocated on the basis of need but control would be returned to citizens who would use their power in voluntary and community organisations to hold professionals and providers accountable. Individual choice of providers would be a guiding principle of this system and the potential benefits would include not only greater efficiency and improved responsiveness in service provision but also a renewed commitment of individuals to each other's well-being and a rebuilding of community solidarity. Contestability would in this way serve as an incentive to providers to maintain high levels of performance, particularly through the ability of users to move to alternative providers.

Applied to the NHS, this could mean that users would register with a provider (or a 'community health agency') but could change their registration annually if they were dissatisfied with the services available. Providers would be funded on a capitation basis by health authorities and would be responsible for meeting all needs within the budget allocated. A range of providers would be available each offering a comprehensive package of primary and community health services. These community health agencies would be democratically self-governing and would be managed jointly by professionals and users. They would be based on primary and community health services because it is these services that most users need most of the time and primary care is already a great strength of the NHS. The aim would be to build on this strength and to achieve closer integration not only of primary care and community health services but also between these services and hospital care. This could include specialists working alongside general practitioners in community health agencies. The services provided in hospitals might in some cases be run directly by community health agencies and in other cases they would be procured from specialist providers with the necessary expertise.

Community health agencies already exist in embryonic form in some of the initiatives which have emerged from the NHS reforms. Examples include fundholding and non-fundholding projects in which general practitioners have taken greater responsibility for the provision of community health services in their area, including in some cases establishing close links with community hospitals, as has happened in areas such as Bromsgrove and Lyme Regis. A number of these projects place particular emphasis on patient participation and community involvement. As these initiatives are demonstrating, managers and professionals within the NHS are leading the debate about the future shape of service provision with policy makers following in their wake. It is only a small step from these developments to the creation of community health agencies which in turn could become non-profit organisations with strong user and community involvement in their governance. There is no reason why in some cases community health agencies should not be formed by NHS trusts which provide community health services extending their reach into primary care. The point to emphasise is that such agencies would be a 'one-stop shop' for users, directly providing care when appropriate and arranging for its provision in other circumstances. Some of these agencies would employ medical staff while others would contract with them to provide services. A range of approaches is likely to emerge and there is no reason to prescribe a single model. Local flexibility in the provision of primary care is a cornerstone of the government's white paper on primary care published in 1996 and the climate is therefore right to encourage innovations of this kind.

As research into the role of non-profit voluntary organisations demonstrates, it would be wrong to assume that these organisations are always more responsive and flexible than public providers. The evidence from contracted markets in the United States is that voluntary organisations are often inward looking and are driven more by the preferences of professionals than users.[34] For this reason it is essential that there is a central and continuing role for health authorities as strategic commissioning authorities in this system. This includes accrediting community health agencies and ensuring that they are capable of delivering services to the desired standards. Health authorities will also be responsible for allocating resources to community health agencies in line with the choices of users.

A further task would be to assess provider performance on a systematic basis. Data on comparative performance would be published by health authorities to ensure that users can make informed choices among community health agencies. Such data would encompass indicators of user satisfaction and provider responsiveness as well as information on the governance of community health agencies and their involvement of users.

Alongside these functions, health authorities would continue to be responsible for promoting the health of the population. This includes monitoring patterns of morbidity and mortality, setting targets for improving health, and working with providers and other agencies to achieve these targets. In this process, health authorities would seek to ensure that individuals took greater responsibility for their own health, given that many illnesses have their roots in peoples' behaviour and lifestyle. Increased choice for patients and greater responsiveness to their demands would be matched by a renewed emphasis on individual responsibility for the prevention of disease. Equally, health authorities would be charged with countering the threat posed by infectious diseases and acting on the social, economic and environmental conditions which cause ill health.

The case for moving away from public to community ownership of health services has been outlined in this way to demonstrate how it would differ from current arrangements. In reality, it will take time to continue the transformation of the NHS but the battle of ideas has already been joined. The application of the PFI within the NHS has thrown down a challenge to the supporters of the NHS and it is essential to understand that public ownership is not the only alternative to private finance. There is an opportunity for those on both the right and left to think imaginatively about future forms of governance and management in the public sector. By encouraging the development of a mixed economy of service provision, including non-profit voluntary and community organisations, it should be possible to move beyond the sterile debate about public versus private provision to a more mature discussion of the alternatives.[35] At the heart of this discussion should be active consideration of how NHS trusts can be taken back into community and voluntary sector ownership on an experimental basis as part of the further modernisation of health care provision. This would help in overcoming lack of accountability in the present system and the remoteness and insensitivity of providers in the old NHS. Over time the public's stake in health care would be reinforced by the emergence of genuinely self-governing community health agencies. With health authorities acting as the strategic commissioning authorities in each area, the public's interest would be safeguarded and attention could focus on ensuring the accountability of the health care professions alongside increasing choice and responsiveness for users.

To be sure, there are risks in pursuing this strategy but if it were implemented in stages and subject to rigorous evaluation it could preserve the principles on which the NHS was founded while updating its structure. The important point is that a variety of forms of ownership exist and a period of experimentation is needed to assess their impact on efficiency, responsiveness, choice and equity. This section has emphasised the potential contribution of voluntary and community involvement in service delivery as a counterbalance to the traditional debate which focuses mainly on the respective merits of public versus private ownership. More positively, there is a real opportunity to use non-profit agencies to reconnect services with those they are intended to benefit.

The funding of health care

However the debate about the ownership of hospitals and community health services is resolved, an issue of even greater significance for the future is the level of funding to be provided and how available resources will be reconciled with the demands made by an ageing population and advances in medical technology. This debate about rationing is a challenge facing policy makers in many countries.[36] In the UK the House of Commons Health Committee has recently reviewed the approach taken by the government and health authorities and has also looked at experience outside this country.[37] For its part, the government has argued that rationing by excluding core services from the NHS menu is not necessary and that efforts should be concentrated on ensuring that existing budgets are used in a cost-effective manner.[38] It is partly for this reason that the NHS research and development programme has focused on evidence-based medicine and health technology assessment. Support for the government's position has been provided by analysts who argue that there is scope for increasing the efficiency with which resources are deployed and that additional resources should not be provided until ineffective and inefficient practices have been eliminated.[39]

While this argument has considerable force, it is difficult to reconcile with the pressures under which NHS staff are currently operating. Whatever the arguments about the future demand for health care, health authorities are finding it difficult to balance their budgets and there is widespread evidence of underfunding. This is illustrated by significant increases in emergency medical admissions to hospitals in some parts of the NHS, the shortage of intensive care facilities, and difficulties in recruiting staff. There is also a backlog of need represented by waiting lists for hospital treatment and the low quality of care provided for groups such as people with mental illness and learning difficulties. Furthermore, it has been argued that evidence-based medicine will not produce significant savings in expenditure and the new scientism represented by this approach is unlikely to convert scarcity into plenty.[40]

On balance, it is widely accepted that advances in medical technology tend to increase spending as they open up new opportunities for diagnosis and treatment.[41] This is illustrated by innovations in transplant surgery and expensive drug therapy (for example, the use of beta interferon for multiple sclerosis) which have added considerably to health care costs. The same applies to new forms of medical imaging such as magnetic resonance imaging scanners. Although some of these additional costs can be absorbed by increases in NHS expenditure, the combined effects of technological developments, demographic pressures and rising public expectations are stretching the capacity of the NHS to its limits. Nor is there any reason to believe that increased expenditure on prevention and health promotion will produce commensurate savings in other parts of the NHS. The evidence seems to suggest that, contrary to the popular view, prevention usually adds to health service expenditure.[42]

Rationing is already apparent in the case of well-publicised patients such as Laura Davies and Jaymee Bowen and it is of particular concern in relation to the availability of long-term care within the NHS. The progressive withdrawal of the NHS from the provision of long-term care in recent years has resulted in gaps in service provision which local authorities, themselves operating under tight financial constraints, have not been able to plug. The consequence is that much of the cost of long-term care has fallen to families to meet and the expectation that the NHS would be there to look after sick and disabled people in times of need has not always been fulfilled. This in turn has led to 'bed blocking' in acute hospitals as elderly patients occupy beds unnecessarily because of the absence of alternatives in the community. These issues are not new, and rationing has always been a feature of the NHS, but the NHS reforms have brought them out into the open and have made transparent the process of priority setting in health care. What then are the options for the future? There are five main possibilities.

The first is to allocate extra resources to health care by changing public spending priorities or increasing taxation. As Figure 4 shows (see page 54), the UK spends a lower level of its gross domestic product on health care than most OECD countries.[43] Notwithstanding evidence that a majority of the public appears to be willing to pay more in taxation if the money raised is spent on health care, and that health care is ranked highly by the public when asked about priorities for extra spending, both the Conservative and Labour parties have been cautious in making commitments to increase the NHS budget in the future. The introduction of an hypothecated tax has been advocated by some analysts as a way of overcoming

Figure 4

Health expenditure as a percentage of GDP: 1992

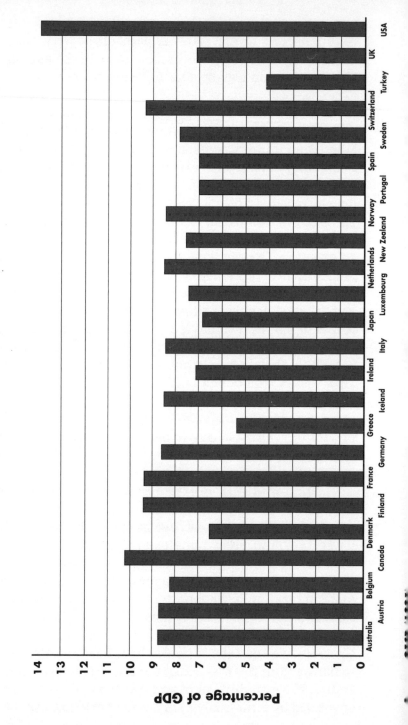

political and public resistance to general increases in taxation and this option has obvious attractions.[44] Yet, at a time when the political debate focuses on how public spending can be contained and taxes cut, the prospects of translating public preferences for increased NHS spending through increased taxation into practice seem to be slim. If, as appears likely, NHS spending continues to grow, but at a slow rate, then it is unrealistic to expect the rationing debate to be resolved by large increases in public expenditure. This is not to say that extra money could not be found through changes in spending plans or increases in taxes, just that at present the auguries are not promising.

Second, it may be possible to increase private expenditure on health care, thereby bringing the UK into line with other OECD countries which on average raise a higher proportion of total expenditure on health care through private sources than the UK (see Figure 5 on page 56).[45] This could be done by increasing existing user charges within the NHS and extending charges to new services such as GP consultations and hospital stays; allowing patients to buy additional amenities within the NHS; and promoting the growth of private medical insurance. These options need to be considered carefully to avoid undermining equity and deterring patients from using services appropriately. The costs of collecting payments from patients also have to be weighed against the income that would accrue, as would the effects of means testing. In the case of private medical insurance, the proportion of the population with insurance has reached a plateau after significant growth during the 1980s and the scope for using this route to relieve pressure on the NHS is limited unless governments are prepared to countenance providing tax incentives to people taking out insurance. This has been done to encourage elderly people to take out private medical insurance and to widen personal provision for long-term care, but as yet there have been no moves to extend this to other areas. Indeed, in many ways the provision of tax

Figure 5

The public share of health expenditure 1992

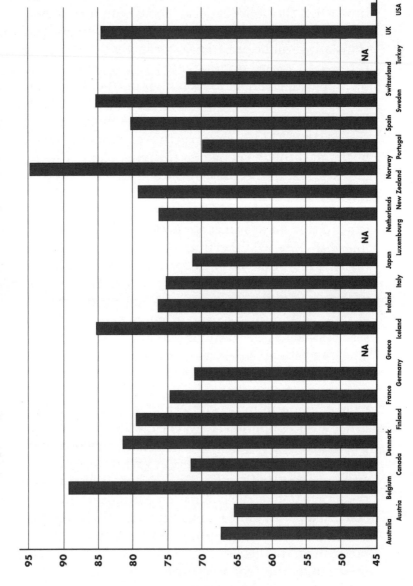

incentives would be a regressive development which could further increase health care inequalities. Private insurance is a valuable supplement to the NHS but it can never be a substitute for public funding.

Third, the scope of the NHS may be defined more tightly with the commitment to comprehensiveness gradually being abandoned. This is the core services debate which has emerged out of current pressures to ration care within the NHS. Stated at its simplest, the argument here is that the NHS should concentrate on delivering a set of basic or core services to the population. Those services not included within the core would be left to individuals to pay for directly. This has already started to happen in dentistry and long-term care, and the same principles could apply to other services not considered sufficiently important or effective to be included in the basic package of publicly financed care. A number of countries have explored this route and defining the menu of services available within the NHS would be a logical if controversial way of addressing the rationing dilemma. Indeed, this may be inevitable if, as suggested above, the NHS is increasingly becoming a national health insurance organisation rather than an integrated financier and provider of health care, not least because the public will demand to know what risks the 'insurance policy' covers. The scope of the core service would be the subject of debate and could be more or less generous depending on the availability of funding. Already there are indications that some health authorities are beginning to rule out certain services from NHS contracts at a local level and this practice is likely to become more widespread with the passage of time, unless additional resources can be channelled into the NHS.[46]

A fourth option would be to retain the NHS as a comprehensive service but to restrict coverage to the retired population, the unemployed and people on low incomes. Put another way, universality would be abandoned and public resources for health care would be concentrated on the most needy groups in the

57

population. Other groups would be required to meet their own health care costs either through out of pocket payments or more likely through private medical insurance. As in other countries, state provision would be needed to ensure that all citizens were protected against catastrophic illness. Those who argue that the NHS should become a safety net for the poor maintain that since 1948 rising levels of personal incomes have enabled most people in the population to pay for health care and if public resources are in short supply they should be targeted on those most at risk. On the other hand, there would be great political risks for any government in moving in this direction in view of the popularity of the NHS. There are also well-known deficiencies in the health insurance market and grave doubts about its ability to offer an alternative to the NHS, even if this were restricted to middle and upper income groups. Tax funding is both efficient and equitable and there is little reason to believe that replacing it with private funding would offer any advantage. This is one of the reasons why the Thatcher governments in the 1980s considered moving away from tax funding but concluded that this would offer no advantage. As Nigel Lawson notes in his memoirs:

'We looked ... at other countries to see whether we could learn from them; but it was soon clear that every country we looked at was having problems with its provision of medical care. All of them – France, the United States, Germany – had different systems; but each of them had acute problems which none of them had solved. They were all in at least as much difficulty as we were, and it did not take long to conclude that there was surprisingly little that we could learn from any of the other systems. To try to change from the Health Service to any of the sorts of systems in use overseas would simply be out of the frying pan into the fire.'[47]

Fifth, it would be possible to limit both comprehensiveness and universality. In essence, this would mean the NHS becoming the provider of a set of basic or core services for low income groups in the population only. These groups would have to make their own provision for non-core services. Other groups in the population would be expected to pay for care directly and this could be mandated by the government to avoid the problem of people being uninsured. Figure 6 (on page 60) illustrates a number of these options, showing various permutations available to policy makers.

Given the importance attached to the NHS by the UK population and the risks for politicians in even articulating, let alone advocating, the more radical of these alternatives, there are formidable obstacles to a serious debate on the future funding of the NHS. It appears that there are some policies too sensitive to be the subject of public discussion and the alternative is therefore to argue that the funding problem does not exist and to cope with the consequences on an incremental basis instead of addressing them head on. Indeed, as recent experience has shown, it is usually much easier for politicians to change the funding of welfare service through a series of small shifts in policy than via full frontal debate.[48] To extend the analogy, the risk of the latter is that it will expose deep divisions of values and philosophy and reveal the lack of consensus on reform. Yet policy making by stealth or obfuscation also has its drawbacks, not least in undermining faith in the political process. At a time when rationing is already a feature of the NHS, and not merely a hypothetical possibility for the future, there is a growing sense of urgency in this area. The key question is therefore how to bring the issues out into the open to enable a proper consideration of options to take place without being alarmist.

Figure 6

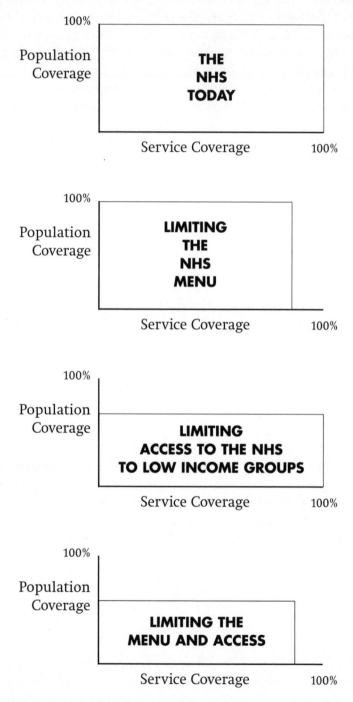

The way forward

Notwithstanding the apparent reluctance of politicians to address these questions, advocates of change outside the mainstream of politics are actively honing their preferred options in preparation for the next wave of policy reform. Supporters of market-oriented solutions contend that government controls over health service expenditure need to give way to increased user choice and additional private expenditure. This would be based on competing insurers operating under government regulation and with state subsidies for those unable to afford insurance.[49] In some versions, there is also support for medical savings accounts in which individuals are required to build up personal as opposed to pooled funds which are then used to pay for the costs of medical care when needed.[50] Singapore is the model for this approach and its experience has been studied in the search for alternative solutions.[51] Furthermore, the economic success of south-east Asia and the low level of national income devoted to public spending have re-opened debates about appropriate levels of social spending in the UK.

This analysis has been challenged in a thorough analysis of past and future patterns of welfare spending in the UK which makes a cogent case against claims that the welfare state faces a funding crisis.[52] Rather, it is argued that it will be possible to fund health care and other social services through public sources for the foreseeable future, given prospects for growth in the economy and the extrapolation of recent trends. According to this argument, in a growing economy public services like the NHS can meet increased demands without taxes having to rise if they are allocated an appropriate share of rising revenues. This is important as a reminder that public spending decisions are the outcome of a political process. It is reinforced by international comparisons which demonstrate that the UK's spending on social policies is extremely low when set alongside that of many other countries in the EU and the OECD[53] (see Figure 7 opposite). As this analysis suggests, there is a choice to be made between adequate funding of public services and further cuts in taxation. It follows that the NHS could be provided with sufficient resources if there was the necessary public support and political will to make this happen. Whether the will does exist is the key question. Put another way, the main issue at stake is less the affordability of welfare services (including health care) than the ability of the political system to deliver additional funding in a climate of tax resistance.

In the immediate future, the most significant challenge is the issue of long-term care and how it should be funded. Recent estimates suggest that the costs of caring for elderly people in the UK will increase from around £12bn in 1995 to some £34bn in 2031.[54] Of these sums, the taxpayer contributed £9bn in 1995 and this will rise to an estimated £13bn in 2031. Changes announced in the 1995 budget have encouraged individuals to make personal provision for future long-term care needs and the private insurance market has introduced a range of policies in this area. Whether these will overcome the weaknesses of private insurance as a solution to meeting welfare needs remains to be seen. In the short term, at least, they will do little to help those who did not make private provision because they believed their contribu-

figure 7

Government social spending in industrialised countries 1960 to 1989

The growth in social spending slowed in most industrial countries in the 1980s; social spending in Britain is below the average for the OECD.

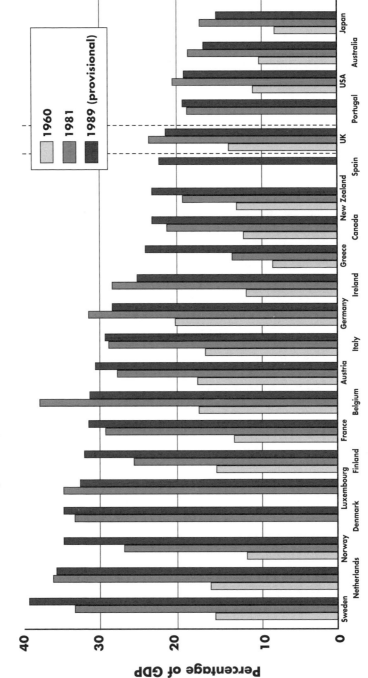

Source: Hills (1994)

tions to the NHS meant that care would be available in retirement when it was needed. It is this group in the population with modest savings and capital assets which is having to use its acquired wealth to pay for long-term care until the point is reached where the state will pick up the costs.

As the Social Justice Commission noted in its report, now is the time for younger people to consider the possibility of insurance against the risks of long-term care and for society to review the merits of personal and social insurance options.[55] These issues have recently been reviewed by the Institute for Public Policy Research (IPPR) using research commissioned from London Economics.[56] One option examined is to fund long-term care through social insurance. This is the basis of recent reforms in Germany where in 1995 the government introduced a statutory long-term care insurance scheme following agreement with employers and trade unions. Contributions were initially set at 1 per cent of earnings and are shared between employers and workers, increasing to 1.7 per cent in 1996. Part of the costs have been met by a reduction in the number of public holidays. The costs of introducing a similar scheme in the UK have been estimated as 1.8 per cent of gross earnings rising to 5 per cent by 2031 for a pay-as-you-go scheme in which today's taxpayers pay for the long-term care of today's elderly population. The costs of a funded scheme in which taxpayers insure by making contributions out of incomes have been estimated as 0.8 per cent of gross earnings for each member of the workforce throughout their working life. The costs of transition for older workers would be £3,500 per head for those aged 40 increasing to £6,000 for those aged 60. It would also be possible to introduce a partial social insurance scheme in which the care component of long-term care costs were met by social insurance and the hotel costs would be paid by the individual on a means-tested basis.

The costs of a social insurance scheme are high. In view of this, it must be doubted whether any political party would make a commitment to fund long-term care entirely through social insurance, at least in the foreseeable future, even if public spending increases in line with economic growth. In the current climate, politicians of all parties are reluctant to make promises to increase public spending significantly and the overriding objective is to cut budget deficits and reduce taxes. This is reinforced by recent experience in Germany where the government is now preparing to make significant cuts in health and welfare spending in order to reduce the burden on employers. Equally, there are problems in relying on private insurance alone to fill the gap, including the expense of insurance premiums and the risks of adverse selection. These factors explain why the take-up of private insurance for long-term care has been limited.

There are therefore attractions in hybrid schemes or public/private partnerships. These have recently found favour in the government which has published a consultation document outlining options for individuals to insure privately for a limited amount of cover with the value of the cover being allowed for in the provision of means-tested care.[57] Under the government's plans, individuals would be allowed to retain assets to the value of £1.50 for every £1.00 of insurance paid out. There would also be protection for elderly people who took out immediate needs annuities to meet the cost of care. The latter would include partial equity release insurance schemes (PERIs) of the kind advocated by IPPR. A key aim of the government's plans is to enable individuals to protect their assets by developing new forms of insurance.

In practice, developments of this kind will not be sufficient to fill the gaps in long-term care that currently exist. This is because the government's proposals are likely to be attractive to some of those at risk but many others will still be forced or will choose to rely on state funding. In this respect, the emphasis on asset protection addresses only part of the problem and the much bigger question of the future funding of long-term care for the population as a whole remains to be resolved. At a time when the UK is much better placed than most other countries to afford additional public spending on welfare services,[58] the claims of long-term care for extra funding merit serious consideration. If, as suggested earlier, it is unrealistic to expect government to fund a comprehensive system of long-term care entirely through public spending, then a combination of additional public funding supplemented by personal contributions is likely to be the best way of ensuring that needs are met. As research carried out for the Joseph Rowntree Foundation has shown, there is acceptance among the public that a mixture of public and private funding will be needed in the future and the practicalities of doing this now need to be thought through.[59]

The real debate then is not about the superiority of public financing or vice versa but how the public and private sectors can work together and the respective contributions of each. This has been acknowledged by Help the Aged in its contribution to the debate,[60] which argues that a system of social insurance in which some of the costs of long-term care are paid directly by individuals out of personal savings accounts would combine equity with personal responsibility, and would also open up the option of individual citizens putting aside funds for a higher standard of service if they so wished. This echoes Le Grand's suggestion that long-term care should be funded by the state ensuring that each citizen has access to a minimum level of care, with supplementary personal contributions by individuals or their relatives.[61] The latter would be matched by government up to an agreed maximum. Another possibility would be to follow the example of Japan which funds long-term care through a combination of taxation, social insurance and private payments.[62] As in the debate about new forms of service provision, there are strong arguments for alternatives to state and commercial insurers to be explored, not least to ensure community involvement in, and ownership of, the insurance arrangements.[63] This is inherent in Field's argument for a stakeholder insurance corporation, one of whose functions would be to oversee a scheme for universal long-term care provision. Private payments could be channelled through personal savings accounts which could be encouraged by government making these accounts tax-exempt. In this way, public and private funding would together enable the costs of long-term care to be met.

Similar arguments apply to the core funding of the NHS. If values such as universality and comprehensiveness remain important, then limiting the NHS to a safety net either in terms of the groups in the population covered or the service provided does not make sense. As successive governments have discovered, there is little alternative to taxation as the main form of funding. Research into alternative forms of health care financing indicates this is the most progressive way of paying for health care and it also avoids the problems of risk selection and cream skimming, not to mention excessive administrative costs, found in the health insurance market. Yet if politicians remain reluctant to increase NHS funding significantly, and if citizens are unwilling to provide support at the ballot box for political parties proposing to raise taxes, it will be difficult to meet the ever rising expectations of the public and the demands imposed by the ageing population and advances in medical technology. In this situation the much vaunted success of the NHS in containing expenditure on health care will become a liability for failing to deliver the volume of resources needed in the health service in the future.

One way of squaring the funding circle would be to allow more discretionary spending within the NHS. This has been suggested by Hutton who has argued for 'a tiered system of contributions above the core contribution, assuring enhanced access to care for non-life-threatening conditions'.[64] As Hutton notes, critics may object on the basis that this would incorporate inequality into the public domain, but the advantage would be to lock the middle classes into the NHS, thereby underpinning universality and common purpose. These ideas are echoed in the report of Healthcare 2000 which argued for keeping taxation as the main means of paying for health care but suggested that individuals should be able to pay additional amounts for extra services within the NHS.[65] Not least, this would increase the proportion of total expenditure deriving from private sources, bringing the UK closer to the OECD average of spending on health care.

The advantage of this option in comparison with increased private insurance coverage is that there is some evidence that the latter may reduce pressure for increased NHS spending.[66] By retaining the commitment of middle and upper income groups to the NHS, allowing private expenditure for discretionary services may be an effective way of generating more resources and of filling the funding gap, if additional public expenditure is not forthcoming. Examples could include extra amenities during hospital treatment, and access to services that are not currently available, such as acupuncture. Providers might also levy charges if users requested a particular drug which doctors determined had the same therapeutic properties as an alternative but was more expensive to prescribe, or to provide services demanded by patients in circumstances in which there was no clinical reason to provide these services (an example would be circumcision performed on religious or cultural grounds). In this way, public and private financing could contribute together to the funding of an adequate level of services.

What then of the argument that explicit rationing should replace implicit rationing? In thinking through this issue, it is important to recognise that the scope for explicit rationing is constrained both by public expectations that the NHS should provide care 'from the cradle to the grave' and by international experience. Of those health care systems that have attempted to define core services, only Oregon has made real progress and even in this case the core services apply only to poor and low income groups covered by the Medicaid programme.

Elsewhere politicians have backed away from drawing up lists of services to be funded or to be excluded from funding. Echoing experience in the United Kingdom, where the Secretary of State for Health has advised health authorities to avoid 'blanket exclusions' of services from their contracts, policy makers in countries such as the Netherlands, New Zealand and Sweden have focused instead on using scarce health care resources on interventions of proven clinical effectiveness.

Given that virtually all treatments are likely to benefit some patients, rationing health care by developing clinical guidelines is a more defensible strategy than rationing by exclusions Oregon-style. And if, as Klein and colleagues argue, defining core services is akin to the search for the Holy Grail, then it may be more productive to concentrate on strengthening the process by which priorities are set than dissipating effort on ever more complex technical analyses.[67] This includes finding ways of engaging the public in debating priorities and ensuring openness and transparency in decision-making. If priority setting is inescapable then it is vital to demonstrate that decisions have legitimacy and are informed both by evidence and by values drawn from public consultation. Rationing is the key challenge facing policy makers in the future, whatever the outcome of the next election, and a strong case can be made for the establishment of a national committee to advise politicians on priority setting and to introduce greater independence and transparency into the debate. This would follow the example of countries like New Zealand which have established precisely this kind of mechanism. Not least, a national committee on priority setting would make rationing by stealth more difficult and it would serve as a forum in which hard choices could be considered. As Oregon found, one of the consequences of explicit rationing may be to channel extra resources into health care by demonstrating where care is being denied. Similarly, in the UK, an open debate about health service priorities, overseen by an independent body, would make it more difficult for politicians to withdraw services from the NHS menu (as is happening with long-term care) without proper discussion.

This may help explain why neither Conservative nor Labour politicians have lent their support to this suggestion, at least so far. Yet if a national committee on priority setting is rejected, the onus is on politicians to explain how decisions will be made. The current policy of establishing a broad national framework of priorities and allowing health authorities to interpret these priorities at a local level and to take responsibility for difficult decisions is convenient for politicians but is difficult to reconcile with a national health service in which the Health Secretary is accountable to Parliament for the provision of health care. It is for this reason that a coherent national strategy is needed in which those responsible for the NHS exercise leadership in priority setting and are held to account for their decisions. This includes clarifying the scope of NHS provision not by drawing up a list of services to be funded but by acknowledging the necessity of rationing and the need to be clear about what can realistically be provided within available resources.

Summary

The NHS stands at a crossroads. The continuation of present policies will result in the emergence of a virtual organisation. In particular, the PFI will lead to a much bigger role for the private sector in service provision. There is a danger that the pursuit of profit will make it difficult to maintain a public service ethos within the health service. The PFI will also have important implications for accountability and control. The private sector will wish to take a close interest in the management of services and the consequences have not been thought through. There are also doubts about the ability of private sector organisations to undertake PFI projects in the NHS.

The alternative is to explore how different forms of

ownership and delivery can be encouraged and old forms rediscovered. This includes developing the role of non - profit providers alongside public provision and as an alternative to the PFI. This needs to go hand in hand with government regulation to avoid the problems which occurred before the state took over responsibility for health services financing and delivery. The aim should be to explore the consequences of returning NHS trusts to community and voluntary sector ownership over a period of time. This would give the public a bigger stake in health care and would result in the formation of genuinely self-governing community health agencies. Citizens would be able to choose between providers, and contestability would in this way act as a stimulus to efficiency and responsiveness. The benefits would include a renewed commitment of individuals to each other's well-being and a rebuilding of community solidarity. For their part, health authorities would continue to have a key role as commissioning authorities, acting on behalf of users to accredit providers and to promote the health of the population.

Public funding should continue to provide the bulk of resources for health care in the future. Raising resources through taxation is both efficient and equitable and there is no reason to depart from this. At present it seems unlikely that sufficient funds will be generated through public sources to meet the costs of the NHS and long-term care. If this continues to be the case then the scope for allowing discretionary spending within the NHS should be explored. As far as long-term care is concerned, a combination of public and private funding is needed to provide the funds required to ensure adequate levels of service provision. These issues need to be debated openly if policy making by stealth or obfuscation is to be avoided. There are no easy choices available and the worst possible outcome would be for the NHS to atrophy as a consequence of a continuing financial squeeze.

The question that emerges from this analysis is the impact of the changes proposed here on equity. In the current climate, the main issue of debate is not how to eliminate inequity but rather how to maintain access to necessary health and social care for all while using public resources to support those most in need. The alternative of privatising health care provision and encouraging middle and high income groups to take out private medical insurance has been rejected precisely because it is inconsistent with this objective. In all health care systems, a trade-off has to be made between values such as equity and access on the one hand and choice and responsiveness on the other. The argument of this essay is that tax funding of the NHS together with government regulation would help to protect access and equity while the encouragement of non-profit organisations as service providers will enhance responsiveness and choice. A combination of public and private funding for long-term care, alongside discretionary spending within the NHS, is likely to be the most effective means of raising extra resources for health and social care if public funding is insufficient for this purpose. Equity should remain a guiding principle of the NHS but other values are also important and trade-offs cannot be avoided. The important point is that these trade-offs should be explicit so that the basis of decision making is transparent and can be challenged.

Conclusion

The NHS reforms initiated in 1991 are leading to far-reaching changes to the delivery and financing of health care. In place of the 1948 model, in which the state introduced a public integrated system of health care, a new, more pluralistic set of arrangements has begun to emerge. For the reasons outlined here, it seems unlikely that there will be a return to the structure which existed before 1991. As Robinson notes in a commentary on the US health care system:

'Everywhere we look in the economy outside of health care we see downsizing, rightsizing, outsourcing, subcontracting, franchising, partnering, and just about everything but vertical integration ... Some interpret the emerging phenomena as holding an intermediate position between arm's length 'spot' contracting and hierarchical authority, between atomistic competition and vertical integration ... All we can say for sure is that this period of organisational innovation is simultaneously a period of innovation in the forms of market contractual relations that permit co-ordination while eschewing bureaucratisation.'[68]

Much the same applies in the UK, albeit in a very different political and social context. A middle way is opening up combining elements of the old and the new, as policy makers search for a synthesis between the familiar and the uncertain. While most attention so far has focused on health care delivery, it is only a matter of time before the financing debate forces its way back onto the agenda. We have noted how analysts of a free market persuasion are already preparing the ground, and there are also moves on the left to think the unthinkable as far as welfare spending is concerned. In both cases there is increasing interest in new forms of financing as a supplement or alternative to state funding. Where the balance will be struck is as yet unclear but with pressures to contain public spending and cut taxation, it seems inevitable that public and private financing will be combined.

In the future, government will have a key role in addressing problems of market failure. The risks of adverse selection, cream skimming and moral hazard are all too real in the health insurance market and vigilance on the part of government is essential if a properly regulated system is to emerge. Nowhere does this apply with greater force than in respect of insurance for long-term care, the development of which must be monitored closely if the problems encountered with private pensions are to be avoided. In relation to service provision non-profit agencies have a role to perform in filling the gap left by government and in helping to avoid the dangers of a commercial approach to social needs. The re-establishment of intermediate institutions between government and citizens, or rather the strengthening and development of such institutions, is long overdue.

In making these points there is no presumption that the role of government should become residual. Rather, government will take on a different role, maintaining a major responsibility for health care financing and assuming new functions in relation to regulation. In the future, the role of government as regulator will be crucial in ensuring that care is available to vulnerable groups and that high standards of provision are maintained. In the health service that is now emerging, government will be steering and not rowing,[69] its aim being to do better by doing less. Government needs to have a strong role to avoid the problems which existed before the state assumed responsibility for health services, as well as to ensure that non-profit organisations really are responsive and efficient in their method of operation.

It is easy to forget that, despite its many achievements, the old NHS suffered from a variety of weaknesses and there never was a golden age of health care provision in the UK. The challenge now is to move beyond traditional dichotomies in the health care debate to explore how the principles of a national health service can be maintained while its structure is modernised. This involves a health service in which public and private play a part but where community and voluntary traditions are more significant. It also involves using contestability to ensure that scarce public resources are used efficiently while enabling services to be planned and co-ordinated. In the health service of the future there needs to be centralisation on some issues and decentralisation on others to establish a new equilibrium in the management of public services.

Above all, there is a need to strike a balance between collective and individual responsibility. The importance of maintaining universality and comprehensiveness as values that underpin the NHS suggests that collectivism should remain a guiding principle. At the same time, individual responsibility must be enhanced if citizens are to have a stake in the NHS and feel a sense of commitment to fellow citizens. The reassertion of community control through an invigorated voluntary sector alongside public provision could offer real gains in avoiding the weaknesses of a for-profit culture and in reconnecting public services with those they are intended to serve.

Given the radical nature of these proposals, they should be introduced on a pilot basis to begin with, building on the innovations which are already occurring within the NHS. These pilots would then be evaluated in advance of widespread implementation to ensure that further reforms are evidence-based.

Notes

1. See for example Robinson, R. and Le Grand, J., eds, 1994, *Evaluating the NHS reforms*, King's Fund, London; Klein, R., 1995, 'Big bang health care reform – does it work?: The Case of Britain's Health Service Reforms' in *The Milbank Quarterly*, 73: pp299-337; Ham, C.J., 1996, 'Managed markets in health care: the UK experiment' in *Health Policy*, 35: pp279-92.

2. When the reforms were introduced the word 'purchasing' was used to describe the activity undertaken by health authorities. With the passage of time, it came to be replaced by 'commissioning'. Often these words are used interchangeably, even though a distinction is usually made between the responsibility of health authorities to assess health needs and to plan for their communities in a strategic sense (commissioning) and the more narrowly defined function of purchasing, that is deciding on the allocation of resources and the placing of contracts with providers.

3. See for example Hunter, D.J., 1980, *Coping with uncertainty*, John Wiley, Chichester; Harrison, S., 1988, *Managing the national health service*, Chapman and Hall, London; Klein, R., 1995, *The new politics of the NHS*, Longman, London; Ham, C.J., 1981, *Policy making in the NHS: a case study of the Leeds Regional Hospital Board*, Macmillan, London.

4. For accounts of the evolution of the NHS review see Butler, J., 1992, *Patients, policies and politics*,

Open University Press, Buckingham; and Timmins, N., 1995, *The five giants. A biography of the welfare state*, HarperCollins, London.

5. Enthoven, A.C., 1985, *Reflections on the management of the NHS*, Nuffield Provincial Hospitals Trust, London.

6. Secretary of State for Health and others, 1989, *Working for patients*, HMSO, London.

7. Ham, C.J., 1994, 'Where now for the NHS reforms?' in *British Medical Journal* 309: pp352-3.

8. Ham, C.J., 1996, 'Population-centred and patient-focused purchasing' in *The Milbank Quarterly*, 74: pp191-214.

9. Secretary of State for Health, 1992, *The health of the nation*, HMSO, London.

10. Audit Commission, 1996, *What the doctor ordered*, HMSO, London.

11. Department of Health, 1996, *The NHS performance guide* 1995-96.

12. See Radical Statistics Health Group, 1992, 'NHS Reforms: the first six months – proof of progress or a statistical smokescreen?' in *British Medical Journal* 304: pp705-9; and 1995, 'NHS 'indicators of success': what do they tell us?' in *British Medical Journal* 310: pp1045-50.

13. For a positive account of fundholding see Glennerster, H., Matsaganis, M., and Owens, P.,

with Hancock, S., 1994, *Implementing GP fundholding*, Open University Press, Buckingham. For a more critical assessment see Coulter, A., 1995, 'General practice fundholding: time for a cool appraisal' in *British Journal of General Practice* 45: pp119-20.

14. Labour Party, 1995, *Renewing the NHS*, London.

15. Ham, C. J., 1990, *Holding on while letting go*, King's Fund College, London.

16. Ham, C. J., 1996, 'Contestability: a middle path for health care' in *British Medical Journal*, 312: pp70-1.

17. For example, a number of LSE social policy academics who have advised the Labour Party have commented favourably on fundholding, including Howard Glennerster, Julian Le Grand and Brian Abel-Smith.

18. See Shapiro, J., 1994, *Shared purchasing and collaborative commissioning*, National Association of Health Authorities and Trusts, Birmingham; and Shapiro, J., Smith, J., and Walsh, N., 1996, *Approaches to commissioning: the dynamics of diversity*, National Association of Health Authorities and Trusts, Birmingham.

19. Audit Commission, 1996, *What the doctor ordered*, HMSO, London.

20. This is the Bromsgrove total

purchasing project in Worcestershire set up jointly by general practitioners in four practices with the support of the health authority. The project involves a partnership between the GPs and the health authority and in many respects is an example of locality commissioning by another name.

21. Ham, C.J., 1996, 'Bureaucrats under the scalpel' in *The Independent*, 9 July.

22. Ham, C.J., 1994, 'Where now for the NHS reforms?' in *British Medical Journal*.

23. Bottomley, V., 1994, 'National health, local dynamic' in *The Independent*, 22 August.

24. Ham, C. J., 1995, 'Profiting from the NHS' in *British Medical Journal*, 310: pp415-6; and Ham, C.J., 1995, 'Private finance, public risk' in *British Medical Journal,* 311: p1450.

25. OECD, 1992, *The Reform of health care: a comparative analysis of seven OECD countries*, Paris.

26. The Co-operative Bank, 1995, *Caring through co-operation,* Manchester.

27. Yates, J., 1995, *Private eye, heart and hip,* Churchill Livingstone, Edinburgh.

28. Hayward, A., 1996, 'St Bartholomew's Hospital – a shut and open case' in *British Journal of Health Care Management*, 2: pp125-8.

29. This suggestion was made at the annual conference of the Institute of Health Services Management in June 1996. See Brindle, D., 1996, 'Plan to 'give away' cottage hospitals' in *The Guardian*, 8 June.

30. Nuffield Provincial Hospitals Trust, 1946, *The hospital surveys: the Domesday Book of the hospital service*, Oxford University Press, London.

31. Prochaska, F., 1988, *The voluntary impulse*, Faber and Faber, London.

32. Hirst P., 1994, *Associative democracy*, Polity Press, Cambridge.

33. Hirst P., 1994, *Associative democracy*, Polity Press, Cambridge.

34. Smith, S.R. and Lipsky, M., 1993, *Nonprofits for hire*, Harvard University Press, Cambridge, Massachusetts.

35. For related arguments along these lines see Pollard, S., Liddle, T., and Thompson, B., 1994, *Towards a more co-operative society*, Independent Healthcare Association, London; and also Jones, K., 1995, *Accountability not ownership – Labour and the NHS*, Fabian Society, London.

36. Honigsbaum, F., Calltorp, J., Ham, C.J., and Holmstrom, S., 1995, *Priority setting processes for healthcare*, Radcliffe Medical Press, Oxford.

37. House of Commons Health Committee, 1995, *Priority setting in* the NHS: purchasing, First report, Session 1994-95, HC 134-1, HMSO, London.

38. Department of Health, 1995, *Government response to the first report of the health committee,* Session 1994-95, HMSO, London.

39. See Maynard, A., 1996, 'Table manners at the health care feast' in *Eurohealth,* 2: pp6-7; and Roberts, C., et al, 1995, 'Rationing is a desperate measure' in *Health Service Journal,* 12 January, 15.

40. Klein, R., Day, P., and Redmayne, S., 1996, *Managing scarcity,* Open University Press, Buckingham.

41. Weisbrod, B.A., 1991, 'The health care quadrilemma: an essay on technological change, insurance, quality of care, and cost containment' in *Journal of Economic Literature,* 29: pp523-52. See also Aaron, H., 1996 'Thinking about health care finance: some propositions' in *OECD health care reform. The will to change,* Paris. Aaron comments 'for the foreseeable future technological advance is certain to continue raising costs'.

42. Russell, L., 1986, *Is prevention better than cure?,* The Brookings Institution, Washington D.C.

43. OECD, 1995, *New directions in health care policy,* Paris.

44. Weale, A., 1996, 'The life you risk should be your own' in Day, P. and others, eds., *The state, politics and health: essays for Rudolf Klein,* Blackwell, Oxford.

45. OECD, 1995, *New directions in health care policy,* Paris.

46. Redmayne, S., 1996, *Small steps big goals. Purchasing policies in the NHS,* National Association of Health Authorities and Trusts, Birmingham.

47. Lawson, N., 1992, *The view from No. 11,* Bantam Press, London.

48. Pierson, P., 1994, *Dismantling the welfare state,* Cambridge University Press, Cambridge.

49. See for example the arguments articulated in a series of articles sponsored by Pfizer Forum Europe in *The Economist* including Belien, P., 1995, 'Health care: growth sector of the future?', 16 December; and Prewo, W., 1994, 'True health care reform: patient empowerment', 8 October.

50. Bell, M., Butler, E., Marsland, D., and Pirie, M., 1994, *The end of the welfare state,* Adam Smith Institute, London.

51. Ham, C. J., 1996, 'Learning from the tigers: stakeholder health care' in *The Lancet,* 347: pp951-53.

52. Hills, J., 1993, *The future of welfare. A guide to the debate,* Joseph Rowntree Foundation, York. See also Le Grand, J., 1996, 'The thinkable' in *Prospect,* July, pp53-57.

53. Hills, J., 1993, *The future of*

welfare. A guide to the debate, Joseph Rowntree Foundation, York.

54. Richards, E., 1996, *Paying for long term care*, IPPR, London.

55. Social Justice Commission, 1994, *Social Justice*, Vintage, London.

56. Richards, E., 1996, *Paying for long term care*, IPPR, London.

57. Secretary of State for Health, 1996, *A new partnership for care in old age*, HMSO, London.

58. Hutton, W., 1995, 'Forget austerity era – Britain's rich' in *The Guardian*, 16 October.

59. Diba, R., 1996, *Meeting the costs of continuing care: public views and perceptions*, Joseph Rowntree Foundation, York.

60. Help the Aged, 1996, *Challenge on care*, London.

61. Le Grand, J., 1996, 'The thinkable' in *Prospect*, July, pp53-57.

62. Bayley, H., 1996, 'Who will pay for granny?' in *The Guardian*, 26 June.

63. Field, F., 1995, *Making welfare work: reconstructing welfare for the Millennium*, Institute of Community Studies, London.

64. Hutton, W., 1995, *The state we're in*, Jonathan Cape, London.

65. Healthcare 2000, 1995, *UK health and healthcare services. Challenges and policy options*.

66. Besley, T., Hall, J., and Preston, I., 1996, *Private health insurance and the state of the NHS*, The Institute of Fiscal Studies, London.

67. Klein, R., Day, P., and Redmayne, S., 1996, *Managing scarcity*, Open University Press, Buckingham.

68. Robinson, J., 1995, 'Slouching toward integrated care' in *Health Affairs*, 14: p315.

69. Osborne, D., and Gabler, T., 1992, *Reinventing government*, Addison-Wesley, Reading, Massachusetts.